Alfie and Pepper
Go on the Narrowboat

The Adventures of Alfie and Pepper

Alfie and Pepper Go on the Narrowboat

By Siân Lewin

Illustrations by Alex Robins

Wishing my son in law Billy Lawson
strength and fortitude in his recovery.
We are all there for you.
With much love xx

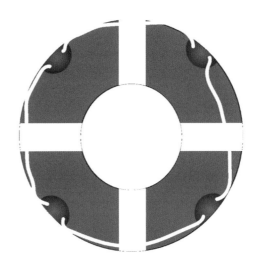

Alfie and Pepper were fast asleep in their beds when they heard the kitchen door open.

Alfie yawned and put his head under the blanket like always, whilst Pepper ran to the door. The only thing that would get Alfie out of bed was the sound of his biscuits being dropped in his bowl.

"Right, Alfie and Pepper," said their master. "Today we are going on a holiday for a few days. We are going on a narrowboat!"

"What's a narrowboat?" barked Alfie to Pepper.

"A narrowboat usually goes on a canal, sometimes for a holiday and also for carrying goods to people living on the canal," barked Pepper. "We will have a fun time, Alfie, there's so much to see on the canal!"

Master packed the car up and they set off towards the canal, which was a short drive away from their home.

They all got out of the car, Master making sure both dogs were on the lead. They walked towards the marina, where all the narrowboats were kept. Master picked up the the keys and they headed towards the boats.

They found their boat, which was a bright blue colour with lots of flowers painted on it. The name on the side was Bluebell.

"All the boats are given a name," barked Pepper. "I guess ours is because of its colour."

"Let's put your life jackets on, Alfie and Pepper," said Master.

"What's a life jacket?" barked Alfie.

"Well, although you can swim, Alfie, there are some dangerous areas on a canal if you fall in and you might get pulled away from the boat," barked Pepper. "A life jacket helps you float in the water."

Alfie liked his shiny red life jacket. He felt very important and, most of all, safe.

Master moved the narrowboat onto the main canal and they started their adventure.

Alfie and Pepper looked onto the water and saw lots of ducklings with their parents, all paddling through the water as the narrowboat floated by.

"Oh look, Alfie," barked Pepper, "there is a swan with her cygnets. Aren't they lovely?"

Alfie was transfixed, looking at an animal that was sitting calmly on the side of the canal.

"That's a water vole," barked Pepper. "Look at him cleaning his whiskers."

The narrowboat then started to approach the locks and Master shouted to some people on the towpath to see if they could help.

"Wow, that is clever!" barked Alfie. "Will we be quite safe?"

"Yes, Master knows what he is doing and those people on the towpath are going to help him," barked Pepper.

Alfie and Pepper sat very still, both with their life jackets on, whilst the narrowboat went into the lock. The water flowed into the lock and the narrowboat started to rise.

Once it had reached the top line, it stopped. Then the gates at the other end opened and the narrowboat moved forward through the gate and on with their journey.

"Well, that was exciting!" barked Pepper.

"It was. I'm glad I had my life jacket on!" barked Alfie.
"I was glad when we got safely through."

As they went further down the canal, Master announced that they were going to stop for some lunch.

"What is a lock?" barked Alfie.

"Well, it's one part of the canal blocked off by another. There are strong gates at either end. Water is pumped in and out, so we can move up to a higher or lower level of the canal!" barked Pepper, who, as always, knew everything.

A brightly coloured pub was on the side of the canal. It had lots of tables with umbrellas up. Master chose a table near the water.

Lunch arrived for Master with a couple of extra bowls of rather tasty sausages for Alfie and Pepper.

"There is so much to see and do on the canal," barked Pepper. "These sausages are particularly delicious!"

"They are so tasty, what a special treat!" barked Alfie. "This is the best holiday ever."

Some children were playing next to them with a small puppy; a little furry bundle.

"Oh, isn't she cute?" barked Pepper. "I wonder what her name is?"

"My name is Lottie!" yelped the puppy.

"Hi Lottie, this is Alfie and I am Pepper," barked Pepper. "We are on holiday and having a wonderful time on the canal, staying on Bluebell, our beautiful narrowboat over there."

"I live here at the pub," yelped Lottie. "I have met so many new friends. It's lovely to meet you and Alfie."

Master then said it was time to get back on the narrowboat, so the dogs said goodbye to their new friend Lottie.

Once back on the narrowboat, Alfie and Pepper sat watching the canal, looking for more animals that lived on and by it.

There were a couple of people fishing on the bank. One of the fishermen waved at the dogs. Alfie and Pepper loved being waved at and wagged their tails in response.

A large bird landed on the side of a nearby boat. It was a heron with a huge beak.

"That is a very big bird," barked Alfie. "Do you think it's looking for treats?"

"More like some fish for its supper," barked Pepper. The heron flew off, much to Alfie's relief; he was worried it might eat his treats, even though Pepper said it only ate fish!

A little while later, Master pulled Bluebell over to the side and moored up for the night.

"Well, this has been a lovely day," barked Pepper. "The canal is such a fun place. It was nice to meet Lottie too!"

The dogs got into their beds and, before you could say 'ahoy there', both dogs were fast asleep.